Begin with YES

Action Planner

Chart your course.
Track your progress.
Make dreams happen!

This simple Action Planner is the tracking system I use to reach my goals. I know it will help you change your life in powerful and "faster than you think" ways too.

Paul S. Boynton

ISBN: 0-9981718-0-8

ISBN-13: 978-0-9981718-0-7

Published by: Toby Dog Media

Cover photos by: Michael Wynne

Website: www.MyPersonalityProfile.com

I have a small silver token with the word "YES" written on it that I keep in my pocket. If you could find or create a similar reminder for your pocket or bedside table, I think you'll also find it a useful tool to help you stay focused as you keep taking those small steps toward your big goals.

A wonderful bit of Chinese wisdom asks:

"When is the best time to plant a tree?"

The answer is *"20 years ago, but the next best time is right now."*

If you're reading these words,
I'm convinced they were meant for you,
and our timing is perfect!

Foreward

A Note to Begin with Yes Friends New and Old

If you've been following **Begin with Yes** on Facebook or have read any of my books—especially if you've delved into the workbook—then you know quite a bit about me.

You know that I speak from the heart, and I speak from experience. I'm not just writing about good ideas. I'm telling you my story and sharing discoveries I've made along the way that I believe will help others make their lives more hopeful, more meaningful, and produce the results and outcomes they desire.

With that in mind, I want to share a short story about one of my life-long goals that I achieved by following these principles and by attracting people into my life who were willing, and actually enthusiastic, about helping me make my dream come true. (I'm also honored to help them with their dreams too).

I grew up on the seacoast—literally on the coast of New Hampshire. As a kid I remember not only watching mighty waves crash against the seacoast, I can actually remember feeling the ground beneath my feet move whenever a powerful wave hit the steel wall. There was something soothing and grounding about the ebb and flow of the tide, watching sailboats drift silently, and the smells and sounds of living on the coast. It was home.

When I finished college, we moved inland to be closer to my first "real job" as a social worker. As my career unfolded, it made sense to stay closer to work, which meant farther away from the ocean.

To be sure, I went back to the coast whenever I could and I never—even for a second—forgot that where I grew up is where my heart told me I belonged. But getting back there now had become much more complicated, much more expensive, and seemed increasingly out of my reach.

At 67 years of age, my children were grown, my 4 beautiful grandchildren were growing up faster than I could have imagined, and I began revising my short list of life goals. I had 5 big goals that were still out there, and one of them was to live back on the seacoast.

Like many goals, this one seemed pretty impossible, but I knew what I wanted and I had seen impossible things happen before so I kept it on my list. I began to believe one day it would happen.

Now, houses on the coast cost a lot of money. A lot more money than I had. When my parents sold their 5 bedroom ocean front home many years ago, it went for $35,000. Today that same house would cost over a million dollars.

Having worked in the not-for-profit world all my life, the cost of coastal real estate was a major hurdle. I also owned a small cabin in a very remote part of Maine that had been for sale for 3 years, and in that time only one person had looked at it. That complication was another obstacle standing in my way.

My credit scores also reflected some poor choices, some poor financial management skills, and again reflected my choice to work for non-profits all my life. This made my dream even more daunting.

So, to sum things up, I couldn't find a property on the seacoast I could afford. I had a camp in Maine that I couldn't sell. I didn't have a down payment easily available, and that credit score would surely prevent a purchase even if I could find a house and had the down payment. But the challenges didn't stop me from dreaming, or from believing. I had a passion for the seacoast. I had decided that living there again was one of my major life goals, and I believed that the small steps at the heart of **Begin with Yes** would somehow work for me again.

I'm not going to take time right now to share all the small steps I had to take between where I started and where I ended up, but I am going to tell you that I did end up living on the seacoast again. In fact, the pictures on the cover of the book you're holding are from the beach in front of the house where I now live. The house itself is modest, but the view is absolutely amazing, and I've always said it's not about the mansion, it's about the view.

This book is a place for you to record your big goals, while planning and tracking the small steps you're taking to move towards your dreams. You'll be writing a journal of your journey. I know I'm not the only one who listens to that inner voice. And I know that you're here, not only because you're listening, but because you believe your dreams count too.

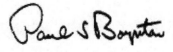

Positive thoughts count.

Positive actions count more.

Introduction

If you've completed the **Begin with Yes—21 Day Companion Workbook**, you'll already have your big life goals established. Once your life goals are identified, it's time to get started on taking the steps required to move them forward.

The pages in this book will help you record your life goals and identify actions you can take on a daily basis to make them happen. Start by adding your goals, then use the "Small Steps" section to list the actions you can take. Breaking your goals down into smaller steps makes it easier to achieve progress, so identify even the smallest actions and you'll find that you're able to make things happen faster than you expected.

On one day you may have 2 or 3 small steps for one goal, and no steps for another. This is perfectly fine and it will change day by day. As you take a small step, the next logical step becomes clearer to see, so add it to list and take that step.

I also use this as my general "to do" list, that way I can keep track of all the things I need to get done – while not letting my next important life goals get "lost" in the shuffle. If you find this helpful, just put a star in front of goal-related steps!

Like with most things in our lives, getting rid of clutter is a good thing. As you complete steps and add new ones, your list will become cluttered. When that happens, simply turn the page and re-write a clean, new list. Re-writing your goals and steps is a very helpful exercise. It helps you re-assess and re-focus on what's important. It also helps you realize just how much you've done!

In time, this planner will become a living document that will keep you focused, allow you to record and celebrate your successes, and keep you moving forward.

One day you may discover that one of these small steps was actually a life-changing moment. Remember, completing just 3 or 4 small steps a week towards your goals will change your life in powerful and wonderful ways.

I'd love to hear from you as goals are reached, at Paul@beginwithyes.com.

Here's an example to help you get started:

List Major Life Goals - think in terms of personal, financial, spiritual

Goals:

1. Find a place to live near or on the ocean.
2. Bring my credit score from "good" to "excellent."
3. Create a group of friends that are more optimistic and goal-focused.
4. Get in the best shape I've ever been.
5. Keep up with all my other day-to-day commitments

Small Steps – What will you to do to move toward your goals? As you accomplish a step, check it off. If you do additional steps, add them to your list and check them off.

- ☐ Find a couple of online sites that list available real estate near the ocean.
- ☐ Figure out how to get copies of credit scores.
- ☐ Make a list of family and friends who tend to be more optimistic.
- ☐ Visit the new gym that just opened close to my office.
- ☐ Begin making daily lists of things I want to get done.
- ☐
- ☐
- ☐
- ☐
- ☐
- ☐
- ☐
- ☐
- ☐

Now it's time to get started

on building *your* new life...

If you're not ready to begin moving towards your dream, take a small step anyway. If you're scared, don't feel like it, don't have time or anyone to encourage or support you, take it anyway. And if you're stuck and confused and just don't know what to do, just take a small step in what might be the right direction anyway. You'll be at least one step ahead of where you are right now.

Goals: **Date:** _____

1 _____

2 _____

3 _____

4 _____

5 _____

Small Steps – What will you to do to move toward your goals? As you accomplish a step, check it off. If you do additional steps, add them to your list and check them off.

☐ _____

☐ _____

☐ _____

☐ _____

☐ _____

☐ _____

☐ _____

☐ _____

☐ _____

☐ _____

☐ _____

☐ _____

- [ ] _____
- [ ] _____
- [ ] _____
- [ ] _____
- [ ] _____
- [ ] _____
- [ ] _____
- [ ] _____
- [ ] _____
- [ ] _____
- [ ] _____
- [ ] _____
- [ ] _____
- [ ] _____
- [ ] _____
- [ ] _____
- [ ] _____
- [ ] _____
- [ ] _____
- [ ] _____
- [ ] _____
- [ ] _____
- [ ] _____
- [ ] _____

It's amazing to discover that despite our delays, missteps and imperfections, we are, at this very moment, in the perfect place to take that next important step.

Goals: **Date:** _____

1 _____

2 _____

3 _____

4 _____

5 _____

Small Steps – What will you to do to move toward your goals? As you accomplish a step, check it off. If you do additional steps, add them to your list and check them off.

☐ _____

☐ _____

☐ _____

☐ _____

☐ _____

☐ _____

☐ _____

☐ _____

☐ _____

☐ _____

☐ _____

☐ _____

- [ ] _____
- [ ] _____
- [ ] _____
- [ ] _____
- [ ] _____
- [ ] _____
- [ ] _____
- [ ] _____
- [ ] _____
- [ ] _____
- [ ] _____
- [ ] _____
- [ ] _____
- [ ] _____
- [ ] _____
- [ ] _____
- [ ] _____
- [ ] _____
- [ ] _____
- [ ] _____
- [ ] _____
- [ ] _____
- [ ] _____
- [ ] _____

If you want the view, you need to climb the mountain!

Goals: **Date:** _____

1 _____

2 _____

3 _____

4 _____

5 _____

Small Steps – What will you to do to move toward your goals? As you accomplish a step, check it off. If you do additional steps, add them to your list and check them off.

☐ _____

☐ _____

☐ _____

☐ _____

☐ _____

☐ _____

☐ _____

☐ _____

☐ _____

☐ _____

☐ _____

Paul Boynton

- [ ] _____
- [ ] _____
- [ ] _____
- [ ] _____
- [ ] _____
- [ ] _____
- [ ] _____
- [ ] _____
- [ ] _____
- [ ] _____
- [ ] _____
- [ ] _____
- [ ] _____
- [ ] _____
- [ ] _____
- [ ] _____
- [ ] _____
- [ ] _____
- [ ] _____
- [ ] _____
- [ ] _____
- [ ] _____
- [ ] _____

Life is not perfect, easy or predictable. Some days are simple and wonderful, while others seem like a runaway toboggan heading downhill fast. But no matter what realities we face right now, we've been given another day. We have more chutzpah than we think, and there's always at least one small action we can take to move us in the direction we need and want to go.

Goals: **Date:** _____

1 _____

2 _____

3 _____

4 _____

5 _____

Small Steps – What will you to do to move toward your goals? As you accomplish a step, check it off. If you do additional steps, add them to your list and check them off.

☐ _____

☐ _____

☐ _____

☐ _____

☐ _____

☐ _____

☐ _____

☐ _____

☐ _____

☐ _____

☐ _____

- [ ] _____
- [ ] _____
- [ ] _____
- [ ] _____
- [ ] _____
- [ ] _____
- [ ] _____
- [ ] _____
- [ ] _____
- [ ] _____
- [ ] _____
- [ ] _____
- [ ] _____
- [ ] _____
- [ ] _____
- [ ] _____
- [ ] _____
- [ ] _____
- [ ] _____
- [ ] _____
- [ ] _____
- [ ] _____
- [ ] _____
- [ ] _____

Of course there are moments and days - and even longer stretches - where things seem to come to a standstill. Naturally, we feel discouraged, confused and stuck. But we learn that taking one small step, no matter how we're feeling, will put us on the path to better days. And so, even in those confusing and difficult times, we smile to ourselves and decide that today, in this very moment, we will begin again. Onward we go.

Goals: **Date:** _____

1 _____

2 _____

3 _____

4 _____

5 _____

Small Steps – What will you to do to move toward your goals? As you accomplish a step, check it off. If you do additional steps, add them to your list and check them off.

☐ _____

☐ _____

☐ _____

☐ _____

☐ _____

☐ _____

☐ _____

☐ _____

☐ _____

☐ _____

☐ _____

☐ _____

- [ ] _____
- [ ] _____
- [ ] _____
- [ ] _____
- [ ] _____
- [ ] _____
- [ ] _____
- [ ] _____
- [ ] _____
- [ ] _____
- [ ] _____
- [ ] _____
- [ ] _____
- [ ] _____
- [ ] _____
- [ ] _____
- [ ] _____
- [ ] _____
- [ ] _____
- [ ] _____
- [ ] _____
- [ ] _____
- [ ] _____
- [ ] _____

The truth is, most of us can't stop worrying just because it's a good idea. We have bills to pay, health issues that scare us, relationships that are failing, and all kinds of real problems with no obvious solutions. So to say "don't worry" seems like almost too much to ask. However, taking steps toward our dreams helps put our worries aside at least for today, and that's a beginning.

Goals: **Date:** _____

1 _____

2 _____

3 _____

4 _____

5 _____

Small Steps – What will you to do to move toward your goals? As you accomplish a step, check it off. If you do additional steps, add them to your list and check them off.

☐ _____

☐ _____

☐ _____

☐ _____

☐ _____

☐ _____

☐ _____

☐ _____

☐ _____

☐ _____

☐ _____

☐ _____

Paul Boynton

- [ ] _____
- [ ] _____
- [ ] _____
- [ ] _____
- [ ] _____
- [ ] _____
- [ ] _____
- [ ] _____
- [ ] _____
- [ ] _____
- [ ] _____
- [ ] _____
- [ ] _____
- [ ] _____
- [ ] _____
- [ ] _____
- [ ] _____
- [ ] _____
- [ ] _____
- [ ] _____
- [ ] _____
- [ ] _____
- [ ] _____
- [ ] _____
- [ ]

Just think... tomorrow could be the beginning you've been waiting for. And tonight, why not fall asleep with a smile expecting that's exactly what's going to happen!

Goals: **Date:** _____

1 _____

2 _____

3 _____

4 _____

5 _____

Small Steps – What will you to do to move toward your goals? As you accomplish a step, check it off. If you do additional steps, add them to your list and check them off.

☐ _____

☐ _____

☐ _____

☐ _____

☐ _____

☐ _____

☐ _____

☐ _____

☐ _____

☐ _____

☐ _____

☐ _____

- [ ] _____
- [ ] _____
- [ ] _____
- [ ] _____
- [ ] _____
- [ ] _____
- [ ] _____
- [ ] _____
- [ ] _____
- [ ] _____
- [ ] _____
- [ ] _____
- [ ] _____
- [ ] _____
- [ ] _____
- [ ] _____
- [ ] _____
- [ ] _____
- [ ] _____
- [ ] _____
- [ ] _____
- [ ] _____
- [ ] _____

There's no finish without a start!

Goals: Date: _____

1 _____

2 _____

3 _____

4 _____

5 _____

Small Steps – What will you to do to move toward your goals? As you accomplish a step, check it off. If you do additional steps, add them to your list and check them off.

☐ _____

☐ _____

☐ _____

☐ _____

☐ _____

☐ _____

☐ _____

☐ _____

☐ _____

☐ _____

☐ _____

☐ _____

- [ ] _____
- [ ] _____
- [ ] _____
- [ ] _____
- [ ] _____
- [ ] _____
- [ ] _____
- [ ] _____
- [ ] _____
- [ ] _____
- [ ] _____
- [ ] _____
- [ ] _____
- [ ] _____
- [ ] _____
- [ ] _____
- [ ] _____
- [ ] _____
- [ ] _____
- [ ] _____
- [ ] _____
- [ ] _____
- [ ] _____
- [ ]

Uphill climbs usually lead to spectacular views.

Goals: **Date:** _____

1 _____

2 _____

3 _____

4 _____

5 _____

Small Steps – What will you to do to move toward your goals? As you accomplish a step, check it off. If you do additional steps, add them to your list and check them off.

☐ _____

☐ _____

☐ _____

☐ _____

☐ _____

☐ _____

☐ _____

☐ _____

☐ _____

☐ _____

☐ _____

- [ ] _____
- [ ] _____
- [ ] _____
- [ ] _____
- [ ] _____
- [ ] _____
- [ ] _____
- [ ] _____
- [ ] _____
- [ ] _____
- [ ] _____
- [ ] _____
- [ ] _____
- [ ] _____
- [ ] _____
- [ ] _____
- [ ] _____
- [ ] _____
- [ ] _____
- [ ] _____
- [ ] _____
- [ ] _____
- [ ] _____

Even a very small act of kindness (like sending a positive thought or prayer in someone's direction) lasts a very long time.

Goals: **Date:** _____

1 _____

2 _____

3 _____

4 _____

5 _____

Small Steps – What will you to do to move toward your goals? As you accomplish a step, check it off. If you do additional steps, add them to your list and check them off.

☐ _____

☐ _____

☐ _____

☐ _____

☐ _____

☐ _____

☐ _____

☐ _____

☐ _____

☐ _____

☐ _____

☐ _____

Paul Boynton

Tonight is a good night to remember that growing older can be a lot less about older and a lot more about growing.

Goals: **Date:** _____

1 _____

2 _____

3 _____

4 _____

5 _____

Small Steps – What will you to do to move toward your goals? As you accomplish a step, check it off. If you do additional steps, add them to your list and check them off.

☐ _____

☐ _____

☐ _____

☐ _____

☐ _____

☐ _____

☐ _____

☐ _____

☐ _____

☐ _____

☐ _____

☐ _____

- [ ] _____
- [ ] _____
- [ ] _____
- [ ] _____
- [ ] _____
- [ ] _____
- [ ] _____
- [ ] _____
- [ ] _____
- [ ] _____
- [ ] _____
- [ ] _____
- [ ] _____
- [ ] _____
- [ ] _____
- [ ] _____
- [ ] _____
- [ ] _____
- [ ] _____
- [ ] _____
- [ ] _____
- [ ] _____
- [ ] _____

You can't begin to take hold of the new you without beginning to let go of the old you. Wouldn't today be the perfect day to begin?

Goals: **Date:** _____

1 _____

2 _____

3 _____

4 _____

5 _____

Small Steps – What will you to do to move toward your goals? As you accomplish a step, check it off. If you do additional steps, add them to your list and check them off.

☐ _____

☐ _____

☐ _____

☐ _____

☐ _____

☐ _____

☐ _____

☐ _____

☐ _____

☐ _____

☐ _____

☐ _____

- [ ] _____
- [ ] _____
- [ ] _____
- [ ] _____
- [ ] _____
- [ ] _____
- [ ] _____
- [ ] _____
- [ ] _____
- [ ] _____
- [ ] _____
- [ ] _____
- [ ] _____
- [ ] _____
- [ ] _____
- [ ] _____
- [ ] _____
- [ ] _____
- [ ] _____
- [ ] _____
- [ ] _____
- [ ] _____
- [ ] _____

Of course there almost no such thing as a perfect day, a perfect thing or a perfect anyone. Perfect only happens when we decide to view the world with a sense of hope, a little faith, and a smile of self-acceptance. And with that, have a perfect day.

Goals: Date: _____

1 _____

2 _____

3 _____

4 _____

5 _____

Small Steps – What will you to do to move toward your goals? As you accomplish a step, check it off. If you do additional steps, add them to your list and check them off.

☐ _____

☐ _____

☐ _____

☐ _____

☐ _____

☐ _____

☐ _____

☐ _____

☐ _____

☐ _____

☐ _____

- [ ] _____
- [ ] _____
- [ ] _____
- [ ] _____
- [ ] _____
- [ ] _____
- [ ] _____
- [ ] _____
- [ ] _____
- [ ] _____
- [ ] _____
- [ ] _____
- [ ] _____
- [ ] _____
- [ ] _____
- [ ] _____
- [ ] _____
- [ ] _____
- [ ] _____
- [ ] _____
- [ ] _____
- [ ] _____
- [ ] _____
- [ ] _____
- [ ] _____

The "secret" to making something wonderful happen today is to just go make something wonderful happen!

Goals: **Date:** _____

1 _____

2 _____

3 _____

4 _____

5 _____

Small Steps – What will you to do to move toward your goals? As you accomplish a step, check it off. If you do additional steps, add them to your list and check them off.

☐ _____

☐ _____

☐ _____

☐ _____

☐ _____

☐ _____

☐ _____

☐ _____

☐ _____

☐ _____

☐ _____

- [ ] _____
- [ ] _____
- [ ] _____
- [ ] _____
- [ ] _____
- [ ] _____
- [ ] _____
- [ ] _____
- [ ] _____
- [ ] _____
- [ ] _____
- [ ] _____
- [ ] _____
- [ ] _____
- [ ] _____
- [ ] _____
- [ ] _____
- [ ] _____
- [ ] _____
- [ ] _____
- [ ] _____
- [ ] _____
- [ ] _____
- [ ] _____

The wind beneath our wings only works when we remember we have wings and we're willing to use them.

Goals: **Date:** _____

1 _____

2 _____

3 _____

4 _____

5 _____

Small Steps – What will you to do to move toward your goals? As you accomplish a step, check it off. If you do additional steps, add them to your list and check them off.

☐ _____

☐ _____

☐ _____

☐ _____

☐ _____

☐ _____

☐ _____

☐ _____

☐ _____

☐ _____

☐ _____

☐ _____

- [ ]
- [ ]
- [ ]
- [ ]
- [ ]
- [ ]
- [ ]
- [ ]
- [ ]
- [ ]
- [ ]
- [ ]
- [ ]
- [ ]
- [ ]
- [ ]
- [ ]
- [ ]
- [ ]
- [ ]
- [ ]
- [ ]
- [ ]
- [ ]

Dreaming about what could be is good. Making it happen, better.

Goals: **Date:** _____

1 _____

2 _____

3 _____

4 _____

5 _____

Small Steps – What will you to do to move toward your goals? As you accomplish a step, check it off. If you do additional steps, add them to your list and check them off.

☐ _____

☐ _____

☐ _____

☐ _____

☐ _____

☐ _____

☐ _____

☐ _____

☐ _____

☐ _____

☐ _____

☐ _____

- [ ]
- [ ]
- [ ]
- [ ]
- [ ]
- [ ]
- [ ]
- [ ]
- [ ]
- [ ]
- [ ]
- [ ]
- [ ]
- [ ]
- [ ]
- [ ]
- [ ]
- [ ]
- [ ]
- [ ]
- [ ]
- [ ]
- [ ]
- [ ]
- [ ]

You are not just "the little engine that could." You are the powerful locomotive that will!

Goals: **Date:** _____

1 _____

2 _____

3 _____

4 _____

5 _____

Small Steps – What will you to do to move toward your goals? As you accomplish a step, check it off. If you do additional steps, add them to your list and check them off.

☐ _____

☐ _____

☐ _____

☐ _____

☐ _____

☐ _____

☐ _____

☐ _____

☐ _____

☐ _____

☐ _____

☐ _____

- [ ] _____
- [ ] _____
- [ ] _____
- [ ] _____
- [ ] _____
- [ ] _____
- [ ] _____
- [ ] _____
- [ ] _____
- [ ] _____
- [ ] _____
- [ ] _____
- [ ] _____
- [ ] _____
- [ ] _____
- [ ] _____
- [ ] _____
- [ ] _____
- [ ] _____
- [ ] _____
- [ ] _____
- [ ] _____
- [ ] _____
- [ ] _____

If you're going to talk to yourself, be sure you're saying kind, encouraging and hopeful things. Then be sure to listen!

Goals: **Date:** _____

1 _____

2 _____

3 _____

4 _____

5 _____

Small Steps – What will you to do to move toward your goals? As you accomplish a step, check it off. If you do additional steps, add them to your list and check them off.

☐ _____

☐ _____

☐ _____

☐ _____

☐ _____

☐ _____

☐ _____

☐ _____

☐ _____

☐ _____

☐ _____

☐ _____

- [ ] _____
- [ ] _____
- [ ] _____
- [ ] _____
- [ ] _____
- [ ] _____
- [ ] _____
- [ ] _____
- [ ] _____
- [ ] _____
- [ ] _____
- [ ] _____
- [ ] _____
- [ ] _____
- [ ] _____
- [ ] _____
- [ ] _____
- [ ] _____
- [ ] _____
- [ ] _____
- [ ] _____
- [ ] _____
- [ ] _____
- [ ] _____

Wishing on a star creates hope. Rolling up your sleeves creates results.

Goals: **Date:** _____

1 _____

2 _____

3 _____

4 _____

5 _____

Small Steps – What will you to do to move toward your goals? As you accomplish a step, check it off. If you do additional steps, add them to your list and check them off.

☐ _____

☐ _____

☐ _____

☐ _____

☐ _____

☐ _____

☐ _____

☐ _____

☐ _____

☐ _____

☐ _____

Paul Boynton

- [ ]
- [ ]
- [ ]
- [ ]
- [ ]
- [ ]
- [ ]
- [ ]
- [ ]
- [ ]
- [ ]
- [ ]
- [ ]
- [ ]
- [ ]
- [ ]
- [ ]
- [ ]
- [ ]
- [ ]
- [ ]
- [ ]
- [ ]
- [ ]

As you begin to trust yourself and your own intuition, you'll begin to move forward into unchartered waters and make wonderful discoveries about who you really are. At the same time, you'll begin to discern who around you can be trusted. You'll learn to go deeper and build more meaningful relationships along the way. Go in peace, but go!

Goals: **Date:** _____

1 _____

2 _____

3 _____

4 _____

5 _____

Small Steps – What will you to do to move toward your goals? As you accomplish a step, check it off. If you do additional steps, add them to your list and check them off.

☐ _____

☐ _____

☐ _____

☐ _____

☐ _____

☐ _____

☐ _____

☐ _____

☐ _____

☐ _____

☐ _____

- [ ] _____
- [ ] _____
- [ ] _____
- [ ] _____
- [ ] _____
- [ ] _____
- [ ] _____
- [ ] _____
- [ ] _____
- [ ] _____
- [ ] _____
- [ ] _____
- [ ] _____
- [ ] _____
- [ ] _____
- [ ] _____
- [ ] _____
- [ ] _____
- [ ] _____
- [ ] _____
- [ ] _____
- [ ] _____
- [ ] _____
- [ ] _____

I am smiling because I know tomorrow morning I can begin again.

Goals: **Date:** _____

1 _____

2 _____

3 _____

4 _____

5 _____

Small Steps – What will you to do to move toward your goals? As you accomplish a step, check it off. If you do additional steps, add them to your list and check them off.

☐ _____

☐ _____

☐ _____

☐ _____

☐ _____

☐ _____

☐ _____

☐ _____

☐ _____

☐ _____

☐ _____

- [ ] _____
- [ ] _____
- [ ] _____
- [ ] _____
- [ ] _____
- [ ] _____
- [ ] _____
- [ ] _____
- [ ] _____
- [ ] _____
- [ ] _____
- [ ] _____
- [ ] _____
- [ ] _____
- [ ] _____
- [ ] _____
- [ ] _____
- [ ] _____
- [ ] _____
- [ ] _____
- [ ] _____
- [ ] _____
- [ ] _____
- [ ] _____
- [ ] _____

When we forget who we are, where we're going becomes unclear. When we remember, the next step appears.

Goals: **Date:** _____

1 _____

2 _____

3 _____

4 _____

5 _____

Small Steps – What will you to do to move toward your goals? As you accomplish a step, check it off. If you do additional steps, add them to your list and check them off.

☐ _____

☐ _____

☐ _____

☐ _____

☐ _____

☐ _____

☐ _____

☐ _____

☐ _____

☐ _____

☐ _____

☐ _____

☐ _____

☐ _____

☐ _____

☐ _____

☐ _____

☐ _____

☐ _____

☐ _____

☐ _____

☐ _____

☐ _____

☐ _____

☐ _____

☐ _____

☐ _____

☐ _____

☐ _____

☐ _____

☐ _____

☐ _____

☐ _____

☐ _____

☐ _____

☐ _____

No matter what your circumstances are, you have the power to heal the hurt, lessen the pain and lighten the load for others. What could be more important?

Goals: **Date:** _____

1 _____

2 _____

3 _____

4 _____

5 _____

Small Steps – What will you to do to move toward your goals? As you accomplish a step, check it off. If you do additional steps, add them to your list and check them off.

☐ _____

☐ _____

☐ _____

☐ _____

☐ _____

☐ _____

☐ _____

☐ _____

☐ _____

☐ _____

☐ _____

☐ _____

Paul Boynton

- [ ] _____
- [ ] _____
- [ ] _____
- [ ] _____
- [ ] _____
- [ ] _____
- [ ] _____
- [ ] _____
- [ ] _____
- [ ] _____
- [ ] _____
- [ ] _____
- [ ] _____
- [ ] _____
- [ ] _____
- [ ] _____
- [ ] _____
- [ ] _____
- [ ] _____
- [ ] _____
- [ ] _____
- [ ] _____
- [ ] _____
- [ ] _____

Think of your life as a beautiful brick walkway that you're building one single, solitary brick at a time. So today, count the bricks you've already put in place and appreciate all that you've accomplished!

Goals: **Date:** _____

1 _____

2 _____

3 _____

4 _____

5 _____

Small Steps – What will you to do to move toward your goals? As you accomplish a step, check it off. If you do additional steps, add them to your list and check them off.

☐ _____

☐ _____

☐ _____

☐ _____

☐ _____

☐ _____

☐ _____

☐ _____

☐ _____

☐ _____

☐ _____

- [ ]
- [ ]
- [ ]
- [ ]
- [ ]
- [ ]
- [ ]
- [ ]
- [ ]
- [ ]
- [ ]
- [ ]
- [ ]
- [ ]
- [ ]
- [ ]
- [ ]
- [ ]
- [ ]
- [ ]
- [ ]
- [ ]
- [ ]
- [ ]

Wishing on a star creates hope. Rolling up your sleeves creates results. This evening check out that special star and tomorrow morning plan to roll up those sleeves and take a small step towards your dream!

Goals: **Date:** _____

1 _____

2 _____

3 _____

4 _____

5 _____

Small Steps – What will you to do to move toward your goals? As you accomplish a step, check it off. If you do additional steps, add them to your list and check them off.

☐ _____

☐ _____

☐ _____

☐ _____

☐ _____

☐ _____

☐ _____

☐ _____

☐ _____

☐ _____

☐ _____

☐ _____

- [ ] _____
- [ ] _____
- [ ] _____
- [ ] _____
- [ ] _____
- [ ] _____
- [ ] _____
- [ ] _____
- [ ] _____
- [ ] _____
- [ ] _____
- [ ] _____
- [ ] _____
- [ ] _____
- [ ] _____
- [ ] _____
- [ ] _____
- [ ] _____
- [ ] _____
- [ ] _____
- [ ] _____
- [ ] _____
- [ ] _____

What if hidden in your biggest challenges were your greatest opportunities?

Goals: **Date:** _____

1 _____

2 _____

3 _____

4 _____

5 _____

Small Steps – What will you to do to move toward your goals? As you accomplish a step, check it off. If you do additional steps, add them to your list and check them off.

☐ _____

☐ _____

☐ _____

☐ _____

☐ _____

☐ _____

☐ _____

☐ _____

☐ _____

☐ _____

☐ _____

☐ _____

- [ ] _____
- [ ] _____
- [ ] _____
- [ ] _____
- [ ] _____
- [ ] _____
- [ ] _____
- [ ] _____
- [ ] _____
- [ ] _____
- [ ] _____
- [ ] _____
- [ ] _____
- [ ] _____
- [ ] _____
- [ ] _____
- [ ] _____
- [ ] _____
- [ ] _____
- [ ] _____
- [ ] _____
- [ ] _____
- [ ] _____
- [ ] _____

Being overwhelmed is a terrible feeling and a wonderful excuse. You can lose the excuses and the feelings by taking just one small step forward! And today's a perfect day to begin.

Goals: **Date:** _____

1 _____

2 _____

3 _____

4 _____

5 _____

Small Steps – What will you to do to move toward your goals? As you accomplish a step, check it off. If you do additional steps, add them to your list and check them off.

☐ _____

☐ _____

☐ _____

☐ _____

☐ _____

☐ _____

☐ _____

☐ _____

☐ _____

☐ _____

☐ _____

- [ ] _____
- [ ] _____
- [ ] _____
- [ ] _____
- [ ] _____
- [ ] _____
- [ ] _____
- [ ] _____
- [ ] _____
- [ ] _____
- [ ] _____
- [ ] _____
- [ ] _____
- [ ] _____
- [ ] _____
- [ ] _____
- [ ] _____
- [ ] _____
- [ ] _____
- [ ] _____
- [ ] _____
- [ ] _____

You have important dreams to pursue. And by taking just one small step towards them today, you will attract the energy, encouragement and vision you need to take a few more steps tomorrow.

Goals: **Date:** _____

1 _____

2 _____

3 _____

4 _____

5 _____

Small Steps – What will you to do to move toward your goals? As you accomplish a step, check it off. If you do additional steps, add them to your list and check them off.

☐ _____

☐ _____

☐ _____

☐ _____

☐ _____

☐ _____

☐ _____

☐ _____

☐ _____

☐ _____

☐ _____

☐ _____

Paul Boynton

- [ ] _____
- [ ] _____
- [ ] _____
- [ ] _____
- [ ] _____
- [ ] _____
- [ ] _____
- [ ] _____
- [ ] _____
- [ ] _____
- [ ] _____
- [ ] _____
- [ ] _____
- [ ] _____
- [ ] _____
- [ ] _____
- [ ] _____
- [ ] _____
- [ ] _____
- [ ] _____
- [ ] _____
- [ ] _____
- [ ] _____

We know life is complicated and we all have baggage. Some of us are packing a steamer trunk, while others travel lightly with a couple of t-shirts and clean underwear. But when it comes to moving forward, we need to set aside our baggage and other distractions, and just for a moment focus on one very small step we could take, and then just take it.

Goals: **Date:** _____

1 _____

2 _____

3 _____

4 _____

5 _____

Small Steps – What will you to do to move toward your goals? As you accomplish a step, check it off. If you do additional steps, add them to your list and check them off.

☐ _____

☐ _____

☐ _____

☐ _____

☐ _____

☐ _____

☐ _____

☐ _____

☐ _____

☐ _____

☐ _____

☐ _____

- [ ] _____
- [ ] _____
- [ ] _____
- [ ] _____
- [ ] _____
- [ ] _____
- [ ] _____
- [ ] _____
- [ ] _____
- [ ] _____
- [ ] _____
- [ ] _____
- [ ] _____
- [ ] _____
- [ ] _____
- [ ] _____
- [ ] _____
- [ ] _____
- [ ] _____
- [ ] _____
- [ ] _____
- [ ] _____
- [ ] _____

Sometimes it's the little things that we feel the most grateful for: like, a cup of coffee, a glimpse of sunshine on a cloudy day, or an unexpected smile. And then when we remember that we can actually create these small moments for others, our power to do good is unleashed and the world is literally changed in an instant.

Goals: **Date:** _____

1 _____

2 _____

3 _____

4 _____

5 _____

Small Steps – What will you to do to move toward your goals? As you accomplish a step, check it off. If you do additional steps, add them to your list and check them off.

☐ _____

☐ _____

☐ _____

☐ _____

☐ _____

☐ _____

☐ _____

☐ _____

☐ _____

☐ _____

☐ _____

☐ _____

☐ _____

☐ _____

☐ _____

☐ _____

☐ _____

☐ _____

☐ _____

☐ _____

☐ _____

☐ _____

☐ _____

☐ _____

☐ _____

☐ _____

☐ _____

☐ _____

☐ _____

☐ _____

☐ _____

☐ _____

☐ _____

☐ _____

The only difference between an ending and a beginning is what we name it and how we decide to see and experience it... and of course, what we do next.

Goals: **Date:** _____

1 _____

2 _____

3 _____

4 _____

5 _____

Small Steps – What will you to do to move toward your goals? As you accomplish a step, check it off. If you do additional steps, add them to your list and check them off.

☐ _____

☐ _____

☐ _____

☐ _____

☐ _____

☐ _____

☐ _____

☐ _____

☐ _____

☐ _____

☐ _____

☐ _____

- [ ] _____
- [ ] _____
- [ ] _____
- [ ] _____
- [ ] _____
- [ ] _____
- [ ] _____
- [ ] _____
- [ ] _____
- [ ] _____
- [ ] _____
- [ ] _____
- [ ] _____
- [ ] _____
- [ ] _____
- [ ] _____
- [ ] _____
- [ ] _____
- [ ] _____
- [ ] _____
- [ ] _____
- [ ] _____
- [ ] _____
- [ ] _____

You've always had the power to follow your dream.

Goals: **Date:** _____

1 _____

2 _____

3 _____

4 _____

5 _____

Small Steps – What will you to do to move toward your goals? As you accomplish a step, check it off. If you do additional steps, add them to your list and check them off.

☐ _____

☐ _____

☐ _____

☐ _____

☐ _____

☐ _____

☐ _____

☐ _____

☐ _____

☐ _____

☐ _____

☐ _____

Paul Boynton

- [ ] _____
- [ ] _____
- [ ] _____
- [ ] _____
- [ ] _____
- [ ] _____
- [ ] _____
- [ ] _____
- [ ] _____
- [ ] _____
- [ ] _____
- [ ] _____
- [ ] _____
- [ ] _____
- [ ] _____
- [ ] _____
- [ ] _____
- [ ] _____
- [ ] _____
- [ ] _____
- [ ] _____
- [ ] _____
- [ ] _____

Like a car parked in the yard, your life is not likely to go anywhere until you turn that key and give the pedal some gas. Sure the Universe will hold the car door open for you, but the rest is up to you.

Goals: **Date:** _____

1 _____

2 _____

3 _____

4 _____

5 _____

Small Steps – What will you to do to move toward your goals? As you accomplish a step, check it off. If you do additional steps, add them to your list and check them off.

☐ _____

☐ _____

☐ _____

☐ _____

☐ _____

☐ _____

☐ _____

☐ _____

☐ _____

☐ _____

☐ _____

- [ ] _____
- [ ] _____
- [ ] _____
- [ ] _____
- [ ] _____
- [ ] _____
- [ ] _____
- [ ] _____
- [ ] _____
- [ ] _____
- [ ] _____
- [ ] _____
- [ ] _____
- [ ] _____
- [ ] _____
- [ ] _____
- [ ] _____
- [ ] _____
- [ ] _____
- [ ] _____
- [ ] _____
- [ ] _____
- [ ] _____
- [ ] _____

There'll be times when people try to hold you back from your dreams. It may be because they're afraid to move forward themselves, or they're afraid of being left behind. Unfortunately their fear can be contagious. The antidote is to spend more time with people who are moving past the fear and stepping into the possibilities that lie ahead with a sense of hope and excitement.

Goals: **Date:** _____

1 _____

2 _____

3 _____

4 _____

5 _____

Small Steps – What will you to do to move toward your goals? As you accomplish a step, check it off. If you do additional steps, add them to your list and check them off.

☐ _____

☐ _____

☐ _____

☐ _____

☐ _____

☐ _____

☐ _____

☐ _____

☐ _____

☐ _____

☐ _____

☐ _____

Paul Boynton

- [ ]
- [ ]
- [ ]
- [ ]
- [ ]
- [ ]
- [ ]
- [ ]
- [ ]
- [ ]
- [ ]
- [ ]
- [ ]
- [ ]
- [ ]
- [ ]
- [ ]
- [ ]
- [ ]
- [ ]
- [ ]
- [ ]
- [ ]

Doors slamming shut... missed opportunities... regrets... mistakes... worries. Expect them all. It's just part of the journey, and in some ironic and comforting way, it's a signal that you're moving forward and making progress, and there are easier moments and resting places ahead.

Goals: **Date:** _____

1 _____

2 _____

3 _____

4 _____

5 _____

Small Steps – What will you to do to move toward your goals? As you accomplish a step, check it off. If you do additional steps, add them to your list and check them off.

☐ _____

☐ _____

☐ _____

☐ _____

☐ _____

☐ _____

☐ _____

☐ _____

☐ _____

☐ _____

☐ _____

☐ _____

- [ ] _____
- [ ] _____
- [ ] _____
- [ ] _____
- [ ] _____
- [ ] _____
- [ ] _____
- [ ] _____
- [ ] _____
- [ ] _____
- [ ] _____
- [ ] _____
- [ ] _____
- [ ] _____
- [ ] _____
- [ ] _____
- [ ] _____
- [ ] _____
- [ ] _____
- [ ] _____
- [ ] _____
- [ ] _____

> When the inner you and the outer you join hands, you become the only you. And when that happens, things begin to unfold more easily and the trip becomes more exciting and fun too.

Goals: **Date:** _____

1 _____

2 _____

3 _____

4 _____

5 _____

Small Steps – What will you to do to move toward your goals? As you accomplish a step, check it off. If you do additional steps, add them to your list and check them off.

☐ _____

☐ _____

☐ _____

☐ _____

☐ _____

☐ _____

☐ _____

☐ _____

☐ _____

☐ _____

☐ _____

☐ _____

Paul Boynton

- [ ] _____
- [ ] _____
- [ ] _____
- [ ] _____
- [ ] _____
- [ ] _____
- [ ] _____
- [ ] _____
- [ ] _____
- [ ] _____
- [ ] _____
- [ ] _____
- [ ] _____
- [ ] _____
- [ ] _____
- [ ] _____
- [ ] _____
- [ ] _____
- [ ] _____
- [ ] _____
- [ ] _____
- [ ] _____
- [ ] _____

If you take one small step towards resolving a challenge or achieving a goal today, you'll be that much further along when you get into bed tonight.

Goals: **Date:** _____

1 _____

2 _____

3 _____

4 _____

5 _____

Small Steps – What will you to do to move toward your goals? As you accomplish a step, check it off. If you do additional steps, add them to your list and check them off.

☐ _____

☐ _____

☐ _____

☐ _____

☐ _____

☐ _____

☐ _____

☐ _____

☐ _____

☐ _____

☐ _____

☐ _____

- [ ] _____
- [ ] _____
- [ ] _____
- [ ] _____
- [ ] _____
- [ ] _____
- [ ] _____
- [ ] _____
- [ ] _____
- [ ] _____
- [ ] _____
- [ ] _____
- [ ] _____
- [ ] _____
- [ ] _____
- [ ] _____
- [ ] _____
- [ ] _____
- [ ] _____
- [ ] _____
- [ ] _____
- [ ] _____

Tonight, before falling asleep, decide that tomorrow you'll follow where your heart leads.

Goals: Date: _____

1 _____

2 _____

3 _____

4 _____

5 _____

Small Steps – What will you to do to move toward your goals? As you accomplish a step, check it off. If you do additional steps, add them to your list and check them off.

☐ _____

☐ _____

☐ _____

☐ _____

☐ _____

☐ _____

☐ _____

☐ _____

☐ _____

☐ _____

☐ _____

☐ _____

- [ ] _____
- [ ] _____
- [ ] _____
- [ ] _____
- [ ] _____
- [ ] _____
- [ ] _____
- [ ] _____
- [ ] _____
- [ ] _____
- [ ] _____
- [ ] _____
- [ ] _____
- [ ] _____
- [ ] _____
- [ ] _____
- [ ] _____
- [ ] _____
- [ ] _____
- [ ] _____
- [ ] _____
- [ ] _____
- [ ] _____

Where we'll be tomorrow depends in part on what steps we take today.

Goals: Date: _____

1 _____

2 _____

3 _____

4 _____

5 _____

Small Steps – What will you to do to move toward your goals? As you accomplish a step, check it off. If you do additional steps, add them to your list and check them off.

☐ _____

☐ _____

☐ _____

☐ _____

☐ _____

☐ _____

☐ _____

☐ _____

☐ _____

☐ _____

☐ _____

☐ _____

- [ ] _____
- [ ] _____
- [ ] _____
- [ ] _____
- [ ] _____
- [ ] _____
- [ ] _____
- [ ] _____
- [ ] _____
- [ ] _____
- [ ] _____
- [ ] _____
- [ ] _____
- [ ] _____
- [ ] _____
- [ ] _____
- [ ] _____
- [ ] _____
- [ ] _____
- [ ] _____
- [ ] _____
- [ ] _____
- [ ] _____

Stepping out into the unknown with butterflies in our bellies isn't all it's cracked up to be, it's a thousand times better!

Goals: Date: _____

1 _____

2 _____

3 _____

4 _____

5 _____

Small Steps – What will you to do to move toward your goals? As you accomplish a step, check it off. If you do additional steps, add them to your list and check them off.

☐ _____

☐ _____

☐ _____

☐ _____

☐ _____

☐ _____

☐ _____

☐ _____

☐ _____

☐ _____

☐ _____

☐ _____

- [ ] _____
- [ ] _____
- [ ] _____
- [ ] _____
- [ ] _____
- [ ] _____
- [ ] _____
- [ ] _____
- [ ] _____
- [ ] _____
- [ ] _____
- [ ] _____
- [ ] _____
- [ ] _____
- [ ] _____
- [ ] _____
- [ ] _____
- [ ] _____
- [ ] _____
- [ ] _____
- [ ] _____
- [ ] _____
- [ ] _____

Often our instinct is to resist change. It never actually works and usually makes our progress so much more difficult. Maybe it's time to try resisting less and risking more.

Goals: **Date:** _____

1 _____

2 _____

3 _____

4 _____

5 _____

Small Steps – What will you to do to move toward your goals? As you accomplish a step, check it off. If you do additional steps, add them to your list and check them off.

☐ _____

☐ _____

☐ _____

☐ _____

☐ _____

☐ _____

☐ _____

☐ _____

☐ _____

☐ _____

☐ _____

☐ _____

Paul Boynton

- [ ] _____
- [ ] _____
- [ ] _____
- [ ] _____
- [ ] _____
- [ ] _____
- [ ] _____
- [ ] _____
- [ ] _____
- [ ] _____
- [ ] _____
- [ ] _____
- [ ] _____
- [ ] _____
- [ ] _____
- [ ] _____
- [ ] _____
- [ ] _____
- [ ] _____
- [ ] _____
- [ ] _____
- [ ] _____
- [ ] _____
- [ ] _____

All of us have dreams and hopes. Those waiting for things to just happen will be waiting a lot longer than those who are stepping up and making them happen!

Goals: **Date:** _____

1 _____

2 _____

3 _____

4 _____

5 _____

Small Steps – What will you to do to move toward your goals? As you accomplish a step, check it off. If you do additional steps, add them to your list and check them off.

☐ _____

☐ _____

☐ _____

☐ _____

☐ _____

☐ _____

☐ _____

☐ _____

☐ _____

☐ _____

☐ _____

☐ _____

- [ ] _____
- [ ] _____
- [ ] _____
- [ ] _____
- [ ] _____
- [ ] _____
- [ ] _____
- [ ] _____
- [ ] _____
- [ ] _____
- [ ] _____
- [ ] _____
- [ ] _____
- [ ] _____
- [ ] _____
- [ ] _____
- [ ] _____
- [ ] _____
- [ ] _____
- [ ] _____
- [ ] _____
- [ ] _____
- [ ] _____

"What if?" will get us thinking. "What now?" will get us moving!

Goals: **Date:** _____

1 _____

2 _____

3 _____

4 _____

5 _____

Small Steps – What will you to do to move toward your goals? As you accomplish a step, check it off. If you do additional steps, add them to your list and check them off.

☐ _____

☐ _____

☐ _____

☐ _____

☐ _____

☐ _____

☐ _____

☐ _____

☐ _____

☐ _____

☐ _____

☐ _____

☐ _____
☐ _____
☐ _____
☐ _____
☐ _____
☐ _____
☐ _____
☐ _____
☐ _____
☐ _____
☐ _____
☐ _____
☐ _____
☐ _____
☐ _____
☐ _____
☐ _____
☐ _____
☐ _____
☐ _____
☐ _____
☐ _____
☐ _____
☐ _____

> You will discover that you have what it takes, when you take what you have and make something happen.

Goals: Date: _____

1 _____

2 _____

3 _____

4 _____

5 _____

Small Steps – What will you to do to move toward your goals? As you accomplish a step, check it off. If you do additional steps, add them to your list and check them off.

☐ _____

☐ _____

☐ _____

☐ _____

☐ _____

☐ _____

☐ _____

☐ _____

☐ _____

☐ _____

☐ _____

☐ _____

- [ ] _____
- [ ] _____
- [ ] _____
- [ ] _____
- [ ] _____
- [ ] _____
- [ ] _____
- [ ] _____
- [ ] _____
- [ ] _____
- [ ] _____
- [ ] _____
- [ ] _____
- [ ] _____
- [ ] _____
- [ ] _____
- [ ] _____
- [ ] _____
- [ ] _____
- [ ] _____
- [ ] _____
- [ ] _____
- [ ] _____

Trust that your path will unfold as you step into it.

Goals: **Date:** _____

1 _____

2 _____

3 _____

4 _____

5 _____

Small Steps – What will you to do to move toward your goals? As you accomplish a step, check it off. If you do additional steps, add them to your list and check them off.

☐ _____

☐ _____

☐ _____

☐ _____

☐ _____

☐ _____

☐ _____

☐ _____

☐ _____

☐ _____

☐ _____

☐ _____

- [ ] _____
- [ ] _____
- [ ] _____
- [ ] _____
- [ ] _____
- [ ] _____
- [ ] _____
- [ ] _____
- [ ] _____
- [ ] _____
- [ ] _____
- [ ] _____
- [ ] _____
- [ ] _____
- [ ] _____
- [ ] _____
- [ ] _____
- [ ] _____
- [ ] _____
- [ ] _____
- [ ] _____
- [ ] _____
- [ ] _____

Loving others, pursuing dreams and aging gracefully is a class act like no other.

Goals: **Date:** _____

1 _____

2 _____

3 _____

4 _____

5 _____

Small Steps – What will you to do to move toward your goals? As you accomplish a step, check it off. If you do additional steps, add them to your list and check them off.

☐ _____

☐ _____

☐ _____

☐ _____

☐ _____

☐ _____

☐ _____

☐ _____

☐ _____

☐ _____

☐ _____

☐ _____

- [ ] _____
- [ ] _____
- [ ] _____
- [ ] _____
- [ ] _____
- [ ] _____
- [ ] _____
- [ ] _____
- [ ] _____
- [ ] _____
- [ ] _____
- [ ] _____
- [ ] _____
- [ ] _____
- [ ] _____
- [ ] _____
- [ ] _____
- [ ] _____
- [ ] _____
- [ ] _____
- [ ] _____
- [ ] _____
- [ ] _____

So often the people who discourage us the most from being ourselves and pursuing our dreams are the very same people who are most afraid to be themselves and to follow their heart. Show them how it's done, but don't let them discourage you from following your dreams.

Goals: **Date:** _____

1 _____

2 _____

3 _____

4 _____

5 _____

Small Steps – What will you to do to move toward your goals? As you accomplish a step, check it off. If you do additional steps, add them to your list and check them off.

☐ _____

☐ _____

☐ _____

☐ _____

☐ _____

☐ _____

☐ _____

☐ _____

☐ _____

☐ _____

☐ _____

☐ _____

- [ ] _____
- [ ] _____
- [ ] _____
- [ ] _____
- [ ] _____
- [ ] _____
- [ ] _____
- [ ] _____
- [ ] _____
- [ ] _____
- [ ] _____
- [ ] _____
- [ ] _____
- [ ] _____
- [ ] _____
- [ ] _____
- [ ] _____
- [ ] _____
- [ ] _____
- [ ] _____
- [ ] _____
- [ ] _____
- [ ] _____
- [ ] _____

The light within may dim or flicker, but it never, ever burns out. Never, ever, ever.

Goals: Date: _____

1 _____

2 _____

3 _____

4 _____

5 _____

Small Steps – What will you to do to move toward your goals? As you accomplish a step, check it off. If you do additional steps, add them to your list and check them off.

☐ _____

☐ _____

☐ _____

☐ _____

☐ _____

☐ _____

☐ _____

☐ _____

☐ _____

☐ _____

☐ _____

☐ _____

- [ ]
- [ ]
- [ ]
- [ ]
- [ ]
- [ ]
- [ ]
- [ ]
- [ ]
- [ ]
- [ ]
- [ ]
- [ ]
- [ ]
- [ ]
- [ ]
- [ ]
- [ ]
- [ ]
- [ ]
- [ ]
- [ ]
- [ ]
- [ ]

With each small step, we discover that we become more powerful simply by exercising the power we already have.

Goals: **Date:** _____

1 _____

2 _____

3 _____

4 _____

5 _____

Small Steps – What will you to do to move toward your goals? As you accomplish a step, check it off. If you do additional steps, add them to your list and check them off.

☐ _____

☐ _____

☐ _____

☐ _____

☐ _____

☐ _____

☐ _____

☐ _____

☐ _____

☐ _____

☐ _____

☐ _____

- [ ] _____
- [ ] _____
- [ ] _____
- [ ] _____
- [ ] _____
- [ ] _____
- [ ] _____
- [ ] _____
- [ ] _____
- [ ] _____
- [ ] _____
- [ ] _____
- [ ] _____
- [ ] _____
- [ ] _____
- [ ] _____
- [ ] _____
- [ ] _____
- [ ] _____
- [ ] _____
- [ ] _____
- [ ] _____

Sometimes the smallest of actions, in retrospect, becomes one of those pivotal and significant life changing moments. That truth alone makes taking a small step today easier and worth the effort.

Goals: **Date:** _____

1 _____

2 _____

3 _____

4 _____

5 _____

Small Steps – What will you to do to move toward your goals? As you accomplish a step, check it off. If you do additional steps, add them to your list and check them off.

☐ _____

☐ _____

☐ _____

☐ _____

☐ _____

☐ _____

☐ _____

☐ _____

☐ _____

☐ _____

☐ _____

☐ _____

- [ ]
- [ ]
- [ ]
- [ ]
- [ ]
- [ ]
- [ ]
- [ ]
- [ ]
- [ ]
- [ ]
- [ ]
- [ ]
- [ ]
- [ ]
- [ ]
- [ ]
- [ ]
- [ ]
- [ ]
- [ ]
- [ ]
- [ ]

If you're not in touch with your purpose, it's most likely because you've been neglecting your passion. You can begin to fix that today.

Goals: **Date:** _____

1 _____

2 _____

3 _____

4 _____

5 _____

Small Steps – What will you to do to move toward your goals? As you accomplish a step, check it off. If you do additional steps, add them to your list and check them off.

☐ _____

☐ _____

☐ _____

☐ _____

☐ _____

☐ _____

☐ _____

☐ _____

☐ _____

☐ _____

☐ _____

☐ _____

- [ ] _____
- [ ] _____
- [ ] _____
- [ ] _____
- [ ] _____
- [ ] _____
- [ ] _____
- [ ] _____
- [ ] _____
- [ ] _____
- [ ] _____
- [ ] _____
- [ ] _____
- [ ] _____
- [ ] _____
- [ ] _____
- [ ] _____
- [ ] _____
- [ ] _____
- [ ] _____
- [ ] _____
- [ ] _____
- [ ] _____

When we leap into the unknown, we discover our courageous, adventurous and hopeful selves once again. And never forget that sometimes a leap is that small step we almost decided not to take.

Goals: Date: _____

1 _____

2 _____

3 _____

4 _____

5 _____

Small Steps – What will you to do to move toward your goals? As you accomplish a step, check it off. If you do additional steps, add them to your list and check them off.

☐ _____

☐ _____

☐ _____

☐ _____

☐ _____

☐ _____

☐ _____

☐ _____

☐ _____

☐ _____

☐ _____

☐ _____

Paul Boynton

- [ ] _____
- [ ] _____
- [ ] _____
- [ ] _____
- [ ] _____
- [ ] _____
- [ ] _____
- [ ] _____
- [ ] _____
- [ ] _____
- [ ] _____
- [ ] _____
- [ ] _____
- [ ] _____
- [ ] _____
- [ ] _____
- [ ] _____
- [ ] _____
- [ ] _____
- [ ] _____
- [ ] _____
- [ ] _____
- [ ] _____

Congratulations!

Now that you've reached the end, go back to the beginning and you'll see how far you've come. As you turn the pages you'll realize just how quickly little steps add up.

Take time to celebrate your accomplishments and give yourself a pat on the back, then get ready to start again!

Best of luck on your journey,
Paul

Paul Boynton

Author and Chief Optimist at Begin with Yes

Paul Boynton, M.A. is the author of "Begin with Yes" and several additional bestselling books on personal growth and change. His Facebook page continues to grow with fans from around the world. Paul is also President & CEO of The Moore Center, an organization serving people with developmental disabilities. He's a popular keynote presenter, webinar leader, blogger for The Huffington Post, The Good Men's Project, a past columnist for the NH Business Review and host of a radio show on Empower Radio. Paul has degrees in social work and counseling. He lives in NH with his partner Mike and their lovable pooch Toby.

Made in the USA
Middletown, DE
05 November 2020